let you do is done in love

1 CORINTHIANS 16:14

With gratitude to Paxton, Pippin, and Gail for the boundless joy and love they offer. To Donna Tiplady, whose idea it was to create a little Paxton book. To Erika Bianchi and Kat Lemieux, for their eagle-eyed proof-reading. And to Jeanne Brouillette, founder and president of **Dog B.O.N.E.S. Therapy Dogs of Massachusetts**, for blazing the way for Therapy Dog teams, who do such heart-work by sharing their dogs' love with the people who need it most.

-- Fran Weil

blurb Available on line ~ Softcover US $10.99
http://www.blurb.com/b/8761307-paxton-the-therapy-dog-it-s-all-about-love

"Hi," he says to everyone he meets. "I'm Paxton the Therapy Dog, and I'm good at sharing my love with others."

Paxton is a West Highland White Terrier, or "Westie" for short.

Even though he is small, and weighs only 20 pounds, Paxton likes to think of himself as very big and very brave.

And mostly, he is. Though he doesn't like it when people make a big noise when they sneeze --- ***"Achoo!"***

And he doesn't like fireworks. Not at all. Or even thunder, come to think of it. Nope. Not thunder either.

But he's still brave, right? Of course he is.

Paxton is also very smart. Though sometimes, he admits, he can be just a little stubborn.

"I call it 'Westietude,'" he laughs.

"But I have a big, big heart, and it is so full of love to give. People tell me that's a very good thing."

Paxton's long-ago family came from Scotland, where they helped farmers clear out farms and barns of rats or other creatures that damaged crops like corn and wheat.

They had a job way back then. And, even as a puppy, Paxton thought that he would have one too, when he grew up.

Though his relatives come from Scotland, Paxton was born and raised in Massachusetts.

He loves the Red Sox and the Patriots and the Celtics, and he wishes he could run in the Boston Marathon. Every year, he likes to watch the Marathon on TV.

Paxton's good friend is Daisy, a Westie who comes to visit every day while her people are at work. And there's Bill and his Husky dog Nanook, who are also his good friends.

Paxton's other good friend is Big Blue, though Paxton laughs each time he sees him, because Blue is really black all over, except for a blaze of white on his chest.

"Why did they name you Blue?" he once asked his friend.

"I have no idea," Blue responded, matter of factly, and crossed his front paws in deep thought.

Blue is a Lab-Catahoula Hound mix and he and Pax love lying out in the sun and howling together whenever they hear fire engine sirens go by.

"It's the call of the wild," says Blue, satisfied, each time they finish howling together. He is pleased with himself for still being a little wild.

Pax loves the way Blue crosses his front paws when he's thinking. And Blue thinks a lot. Paxton has tried crossing his paws too, but his legs are way too short.

Paxton lives with his friend Fran and family, who love him and care for him by making sure he gets his food and fresh water, every day, and that he goes out when he needs to go to the bathroom, and gets walked and exercised, so he can stay healthy.

Fran also takes him to the DOGtors, once a year for a checkup, to make sure he's fine. Paxton's DOGtor is called a Veterinarian, and she takes care of Paxton just like kids' doctors take care of kids.

At the Vet's, Paxton gets weighed, and checked, and sometimes even gets a shot to make sure he doesn't catch any bad diseases.

See? He really is a brave dog!

And when he's done, the nice Vet gives Paxton a good scratch behind his ears and a big, crunchy dog biscuit. Yum.

Paxton doesn't mind going to the Vet, but he likes big crunchy dog biscuits more.

He also likes to go visit Deanna, his groomer, at *Uptown Dog Spa.* Deanna always greets him at the door with a happy pat, and makes sure that Paxton gets a nice warm bath and shampoo, and has his beautiful white coat and nails trimmed.

Paxton's coat doesn't shed, so he doesn't make people who are allergic sneeze.

Paxton is very proud that Westies don't shed. He knows some kids and grownups who can't be around other dogs or cats, or even birds, because they shed, and shedding makes people's eyes water and itch and then they sneeze. **Achoo!** Paxton doesn't like sneezes.

Paxton is a special dog because he is full of love and joy, and it makes him happy to share them with people.

Yes, ever since he was a little puppy, Paxton liked to make people and animal friends smile and feel happy.

As a young pup, after an active day in the yard, talking to the cheerful chickadees, greeting the gentle mourning doves, chasing squirrels and barking at crows, Paxton would come home to snuggle and give tiny kisses to his people.

When his little Westie brother Pippin came to live with Paxton and his family, Paxton went out of his way to make him feel really welcome and loved, playing with him and showing him how to be a good and loving dog, and make his people proud.

"You have to go to the bathroom outside, by these trees," he would say to Pippin, and he would lead the way and show the little white pup just how it was done.

"This is where you eat your breakfast and dinner," he explained to little Pippin, who followed his big brother to the kitchen, where, on a small carpet, sat pretty brown bowls -- one for Pax, one for Pip -- to hold their food, and one big one for their fresh water.

"And if you bounce and whirl around the treat drawer like this," Paxton told his little brother, jumping and turning in happy little circles, "Fran will know that you would like a treat."

Pippin tried the little dance and got pretty good at it after a few tries.

Now the two know how to do their sweet little dance together to get their special treats, which each takes to a separate corner to enjoy in private.

The only thing Paxton likes better than helping his little brother learn about life, and patrolling the yard to make sure everything is good and safe, is chasing his squirrel friends, who skitter across the top of the wood fencing that surrounds his pretty backyard.

Paxton likes barking "hello" at big black crows that sometimes caw down at him from the tree branches on which they land around the yard.

"Hey, Paxton," they are saying.

"Hey crows," he barks in return.

"Hey Paxton," say the squirrels, who playfully tease him into a chase.

"Hey, squirrels," Paxton barks, and then tears across the yard chasing after his swift gray, bushy-tailed playmates.

He would never want to catch them, of course. They are his friends, and this is their game.

One day, after having spent a lot of time watching his big brother take care of him, and seeing how he protected everything in the yard (except for the squirrels and crows, of course, who prefer to take care of themselves), little brother Pippin said to Paxton, "I've been thinking."

"Yes," said Paxton, expectantly.

"You are so kind and patient," Pippin said.

"You have taught me a lot. And you share so much love and joy with people and the crows and squirrels and mourning doves and chickadees. I think you should be a Therapy Dog," Pippin exclaimed. "I saw something on television about them, and you would be great."

"Hmm, " Paxton thought.

Paxton wasn't so sure. Yes, he was good and loving, taking care of his little brother, Pippin. And yes, he loved the birds and animals in the yard, and his people, and also the people they

12

love, who came to the house often to laugh and talk and enjoy each others' company, and rub his ears and make him feel good.

But Paxton also liked to play and run, get dirty, bark, jump and chase his garden friends. That didn't really seem like something therapy dogs should do.

But then again, Paxton loved loving, and sharing that love.

He watched the TV show on therapy dogs that Pippin suggested, and then thought to himself, "Well, maybe."

After all, he definitely could be calm and sweet and loving and not bark for a little while each day, couldn't he?

And then he could come home from being a therapy dog and still play and run and bark and jump and chase things, right?

The squirrels and the crows agreed. "Try it," they said to him. "We'll still be here waiting when you come home."

"Absolutely," said the mourning doves and chickadees. "Give it a shot."

His friend Fran thought he should try also.

And so, when Paxton was old enough, his friend Fran and he went to Dog B.O.N.E.S. Therapy Dog school together to see if he could

be happy and successful as a Therapy Dog.

He was a great student! He learned how to visit people in hospitals, and greet people in wheelchairs and be really careful around people who had trouble keeping their balance and had to use walkers -- all the while, making them happy.

He learned how to listen to children who read to him, and how to help them by giving them all his attention, so they would be calm and confident and happy to read to him.

And Paxton discovered that he loved being a therapy dog just as much -- if not more -- than playing and running and barking

and jumping and chasing things in the yard.

"We knew it!" said Pippin, along with his squirrel and crow friends, when Pax came home and told them.

The mourning doves and chickadees cheered when they heard. "We knew it," they chirped.

Paxton graduated with an official diploma and a special tag for his collar, and a beautiful blue vest to wear that said, "Ask to Pet Me, I am a Therapy Dog" and "I am a Reading Partner."

"Perfect," said Pippin, when Paxton came home wearing his new vest and tag on his collar. "You look really handsome. You are an official therapy dog, and I am so proud of you, big brother."

"Thank you," said Paxton, admiring his vest and his new look in the mirror.

He learned that Therapy Dogs are very special. Their job is just to love people, whether they are tall or short, young or old, healthy or sick, happy or sad.

And the more Paxton visited people at hospitals, schools, and even colleges and universities, the more he understood what a gift he had to share: the gift of love -- pure and simple -- with no strings attached.

Today, Paxton is a therapy dog who visits with people almost every day of the week, and he loves his job.

His favorite part of being a therapy dog is helping kids to read.

Either he and Fran read to the children, or the children read to them. Paxton likes doing both things very much.

Because he does so many visits with children who read to him and help him explore the wonder of books, Paxton knows lots and lots of good stories, and has read lots and lots of books. Ask him about them sometime.

He particularly likes Dr. Seuss books, and books about other dogs -- especially Westie dogs. Books like "Good Dog Fergus," and "Westie Tails."

And after his visits, Paxton comes home and shares the wonderful stories he's heard with Pippin and the squirrels and the crows and the mourning doves and the chickadees, who all gather in a circle to listen.

Paxton also loves his visits with teenagers and college students and teachers and staff during exam time -- which can be really stressful for everyone, because everyone wants to do really well with their studies and their tests.

And so they come to sit with Paxton -- who is always calm, and wears a happy smile, along with his therapy dog vest and special tag on his collar. They relax and pat him, and patting him makes them feel calm and happy too. And if Paxton can help people feel calm and happy, he knows he is doing his job!

At these events, where so many people come to visit with him, Paxton likes to pose with them for selfies. And that is why his picture is on so many people's cell phones!

And every time he visits, the students and teachers and staff write thank yous to Paxton on handmade cards.

He has a whole collection of them, which he hangs near his "wall of friends" pictures -- so he can share them with his little brother and his people and all the people who come to visit him.

His brother Pippin, and friends at home -- Daisy the Westie, and the squirrels and the crows and the mourning doves and the chickadees -- think he's famous. A therapy dog celebrity. But Pax is just happy to be who he is: a dog full of love to share.

The other day, the minister at the church his people attend, asked if Paxton could come for a special sermon she was doing for the children.

Fran asked him if he wanted to go.

"To church?" asked Paxton, surprised and deeply honored.

He only goes to church once a month, to a special pet ministry service where people bring their beloved animals -- whom Pax counts among his many friends.

But this was *people* church.

"Really?" he marveled. "I could wear my special vest, right?"

"Yes," Fran explained. "The sermon is about unconditional love, Pax, and you are the perfect example of that for the kids.

"Because you love everyone the same, and if someone disappoints you, you forgive them completely.

You are what love is all about, my little friend."

Paxton was thrilled to be invited to sit in the church with everyone, and then up near the altar, surrounded by kids whom he nuzzled with gratitude, one at a time.

"This is amazing," he thought to himself, as everyone welcomed him and gave him love.

And with Paxton, it continues to be amazing. Because it's all about love, Paxton clearly understands.

Paxton is a good dog. He is a Therapy Dog.

And he knows that sharing love is the very best feeling in the world.

The End

Partial author's proceeds go to Perfect Paws Pet Ministry's Happy Readers Dog Tutors Program, to purchase books for young children we visit to help them become confident readers.

Paxton and his therapy dog friends are available to visit
and share their love. They are all volunteer, certified,
insured, and ready to help.

For more information on **Pet Ministry Therapy Dogs**
-- an outreach of Perfect Paws Pet Ministry, at All Saints
Episcopal Church of the North Shore, Danvers, in
partnership with Dog B.O.N.E.S. Therapy Dogs of
Massachusetts -- please email us:
petministrytherapydogs@gmail.com

CPSIA information can be obtained
at www.ICGtesting.com
Printed in the USA
BVHW090605161121
621700BV00016B/597